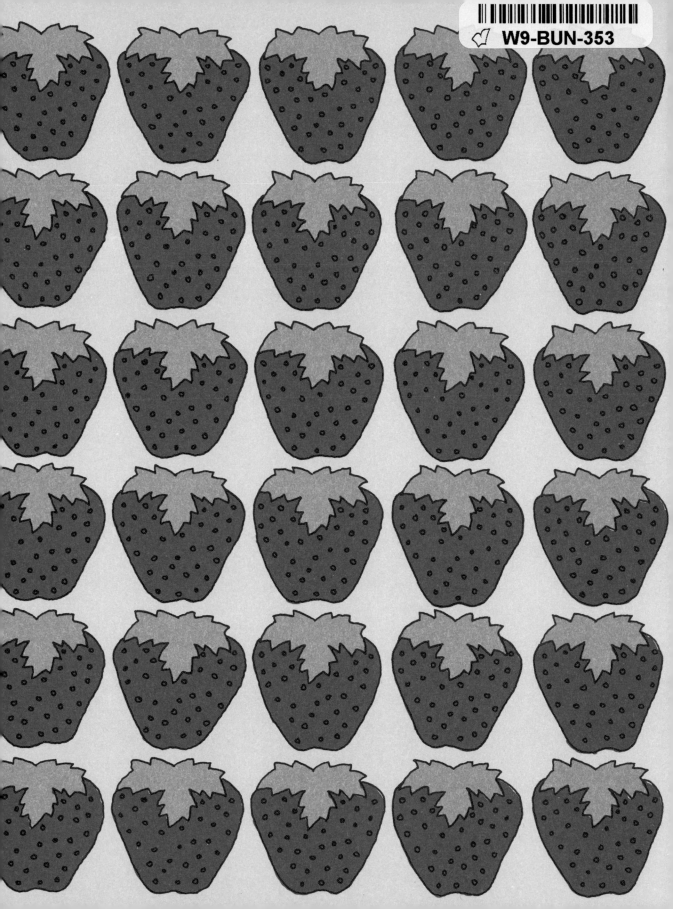

**this
strawberry book
belongs to**

Library of Congress Cataloging in Publication Data

Hefter, Richard.
  The strawberry look book.

  "A strawberry book."
  SUMMARY: Labeled pictures identify objects in such
settings as a toy store, supermarket, furniture store,
bakery, clothing store, garage, and home.
  1. Vocabulary — Juvenile literature [1. Vocabulary]
I. Title
PE1449.H4   428.1   80-16989
ISBN: 8374-0950-0

Weekly Reader Books' Edition

the strawberry ®
look book

by Richard Hefter

a strawberry book ®

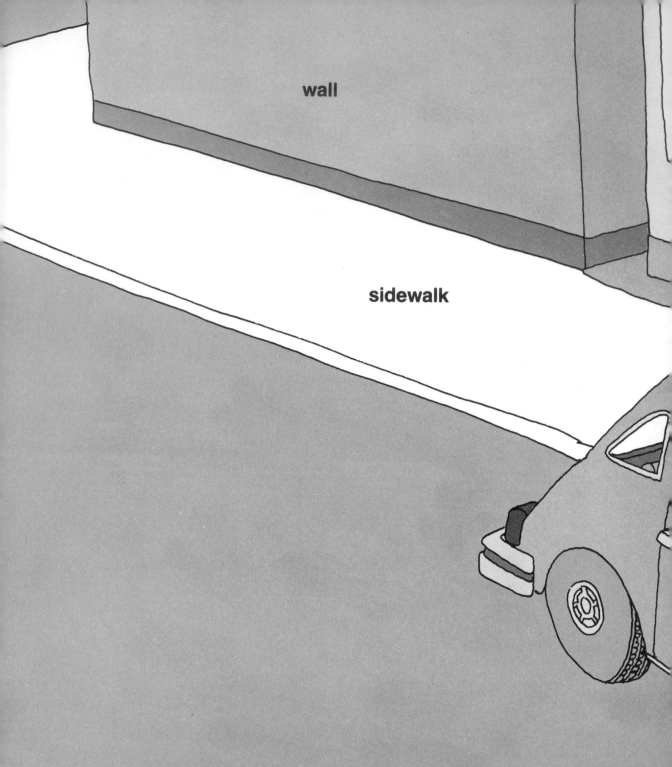

wall

sidewalk

**Look at the bears!
They are going shopping today.**

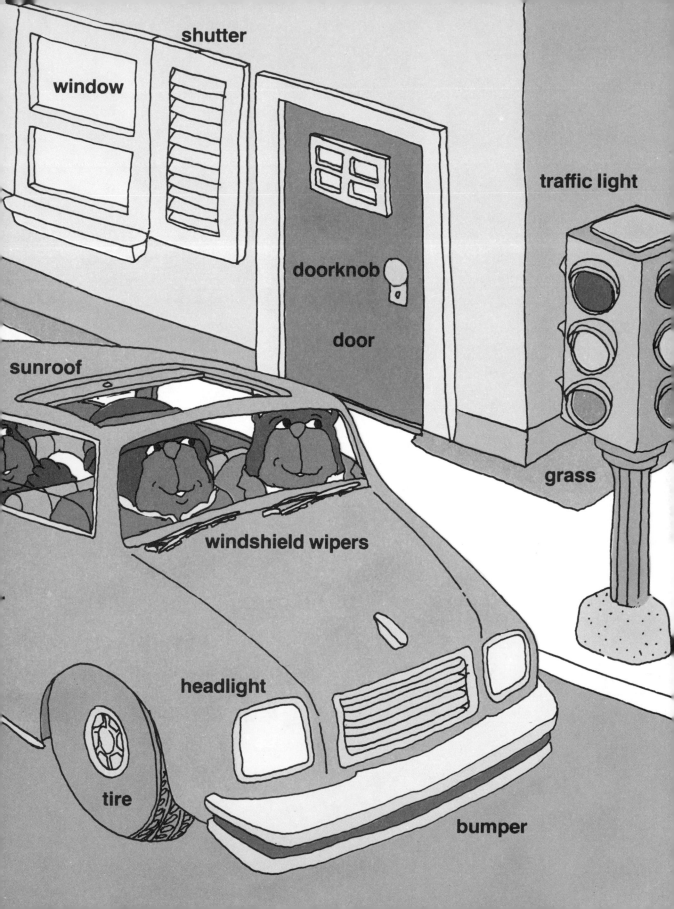

The bears are going to the supermarket first.

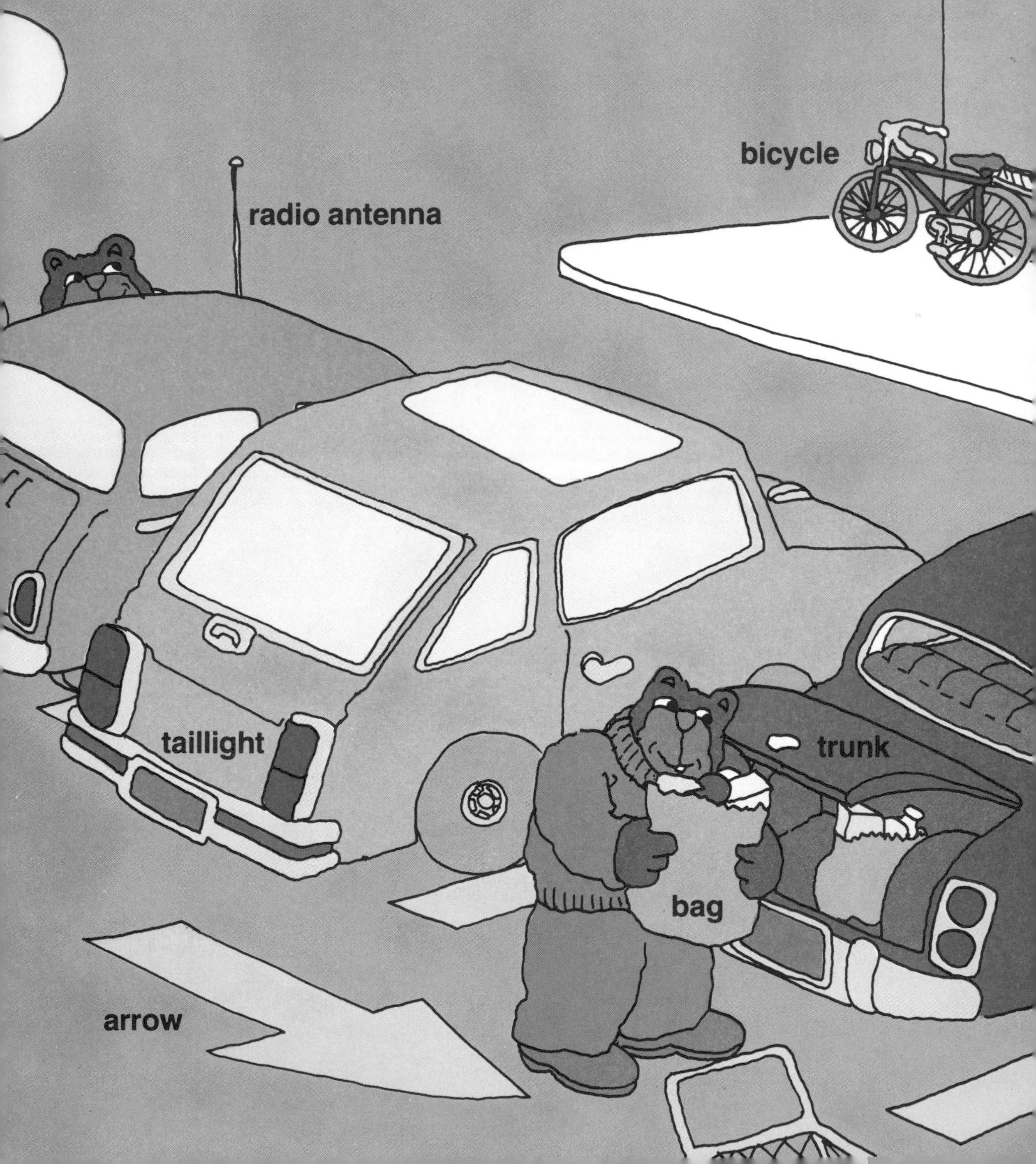

bicycle

radio antenna

taillight

trunk

bag

arrow

hat

handbag

suit

truck

cab

mirror

parking lot

Look at all the food.

pineapple

grapes

grapefruit

oranges

melons

plums

strawberries

pears

apples

lemons

FRUITS ⬆

collar

jar

SPECIAL
HONEY

tie

hungry bear

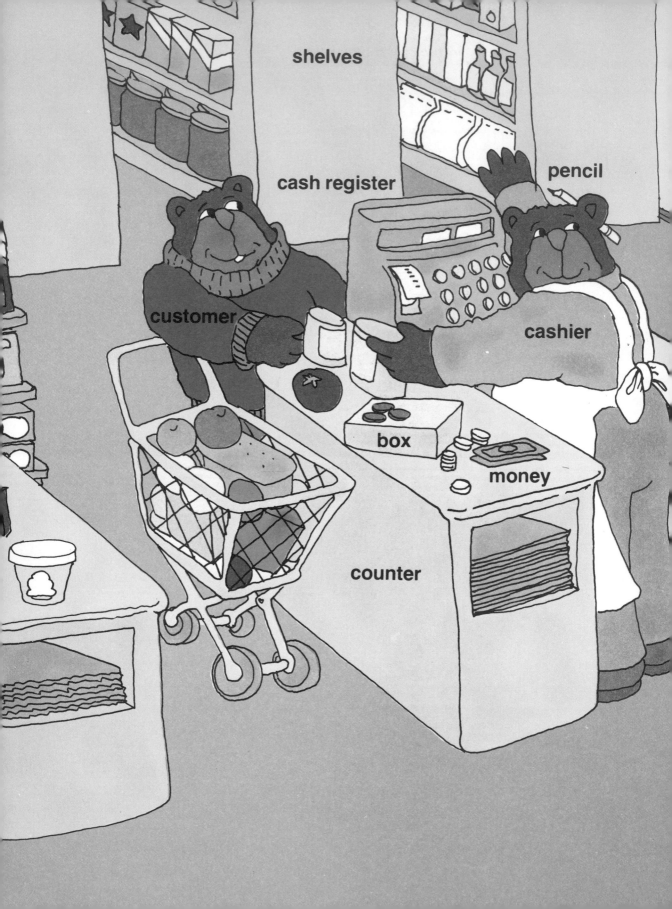

The bears are going to the toy store next.

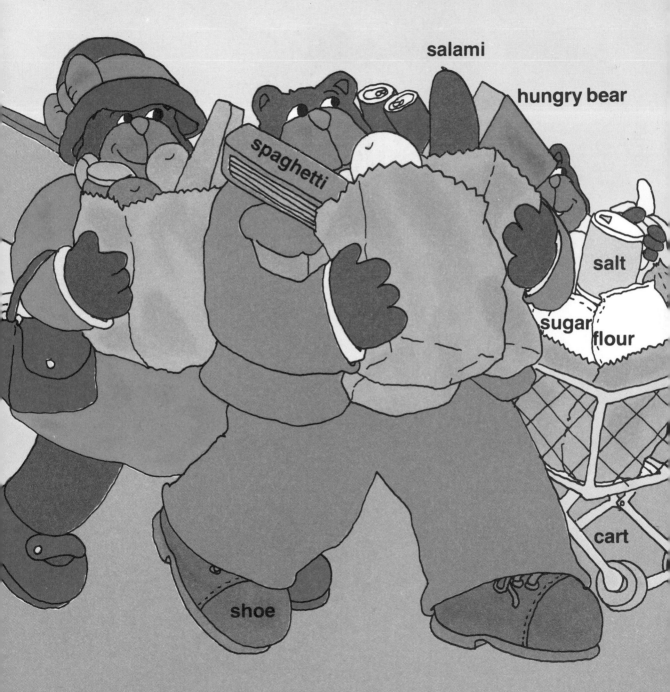

salami

hungry bear

spaghetti

salt

sugar

flour

cart

shoe

Look at all the toys!

pots and pans

pinball machine

dump truck

rocke

control

pupp

car

top

clown

helicopter

skates

ball

locomotive

steam shovel

doll

beach ball

airplane

ddy bear

baseball

blocks

Now the bears are shopping for clothing.

pajamas

belts

buckle

socks

slippers

jacket

sleeve

buttons

shirts

caps

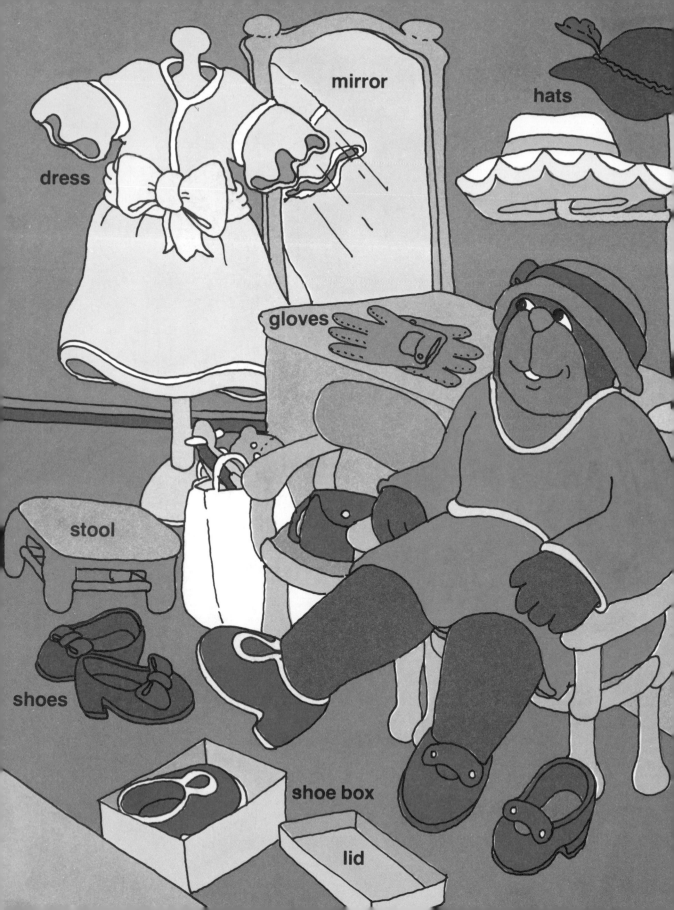

dress

mirror

hats

gloves

stool

shoes

shoe box

lid

The bears are going to eat lunch.

After lunch, the bears look in a furniture store.

clock

frame

picture

lamp shade

couch

lamp

pillow

table

chair

desk

radio

rug

bookcase

books

television

salesperson

chest of
drawers

vase

drawer

armchair

Look at the bears loading their car.

coffee table

rope

The bears stop at a bakery.

wedding cake

pastries

birthday cake

layer cake

pie

buns

cookies

cupcakes

doughnuts

jelly doughnuts

Look at the pretty flowers.

roses

daisy

zinnias

scissors

tape

pansies

sweet william

trowel

watering can

potting soil

hoe

Look at the garage.

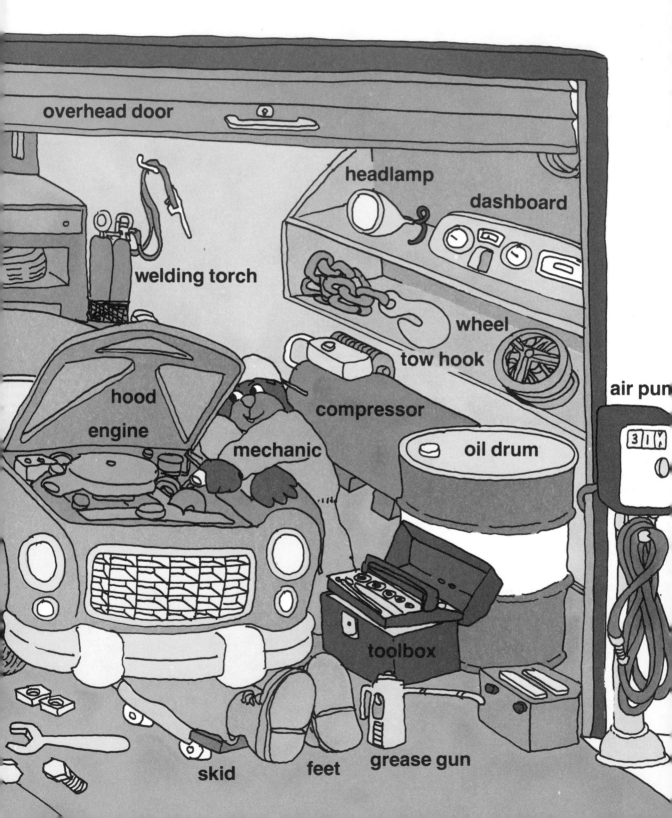

overhead door

headlamp

dashboard

welding torch

wheel

tow hook

hood

engine

compressor

mechanic

oil drum

air pump

toolbox

skid

feet

grease gun

**The bears are going
home now.
Look at the moon and
the stars.**

Good night, sleepy bear.

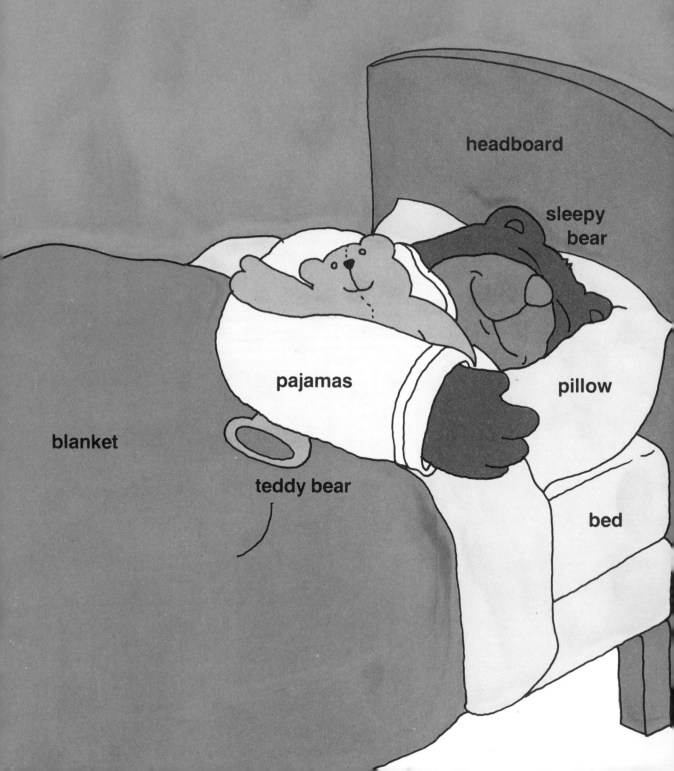

headboard

sleepy bear

pajamas

pillow

blanket

teddy bear

bed

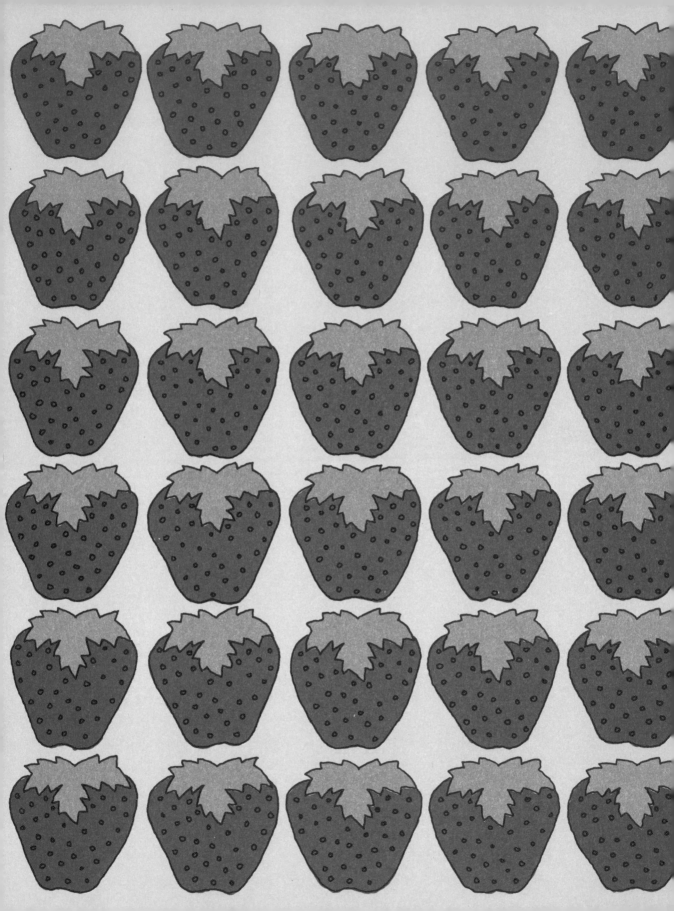